Ukulele from the Beginning

Book 2

Published by
Chester Music Limited
14-15 Berners Street,
London W1T 3LJ, UK.

Exclusive Distributors:
Music Sales Limited
Distribution Centre, Newmarket Road,
Bury St Edmunds, Suffolk IP33 3YB, UK.

Music Sales Corporation
257 Park Avenue South, New York, NY10010
United States of America.

Music Sales Pty Limited
20 Resolution Drive
Caringbah, NSW 2229,
Australia.

This book © Copyright 2010 Chester Music.
All rights reserved. International copyright secured.

Unauthorised reproduction of any part of this publication by any means
including photocopying is an infringement of copyright.

Written by Christopher Hussey
Illustrations by Benedict Siddle
Processing and layout by Camden Music, London.
Edited by Rachel Lindley

Printed in the EU.

www.musicsales.com

About the book

Versatile and adaptable, the ukulele has been around since the late 19th century and is now enjoying a remarkable surge in popularity, particularly in the classroom. It's inexpensive, easy to learn and suitable for playing all kinds of music.

This book reinforces and builds upon what you've already learnt in *Ukulele From The Beginning Book 1*, introducing new chords and strumming patterns as well as reminding you of familiar ones. A new style of accompaniment called 'fingerpicking' is introduced later, so that by the end of this book you will be able to impress everyone with a variety of ukulele-playing techniques!

Any teacher, with or without musical knowledge, will discover that by using *Ukulele from the Beginning* it's simple to teach basic chords and fingerpicking by playing along with well-known songs. The ukulele is a great place to start enjoying music in the classroom and this book makes the process a pleasure for teacher and children alike.

Contents

Getting started

Playing your ukulele can provide a great accompaniment to singing so, just like *Book 1*, this book is full of lots of well-known songs that you can sing and play along to.

You don't need to read music, but we have written out the tunes in this book under the chord symbols to help you know when to play — or they could be played on another instrument.

You'll need to tune your ukulele first of all. You should do this each time before you play your instrument. Remember from *Book 1* that the ukulele's four strings are tuned to the following notes:

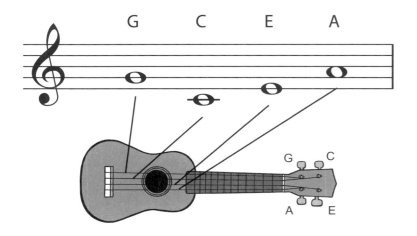

You can find these notes on a piano or you can use an electronic tuner. Turn each tuning peg until the string reaches the same pitch as the tuning note — turning clockwise makes the note higher, anti-clockwise makes it lower.

Strumming and chords

In *Book 1* you learnt how to strum your ukulele, using a **downstroke** or an **upstroke** to play all four strings at once.

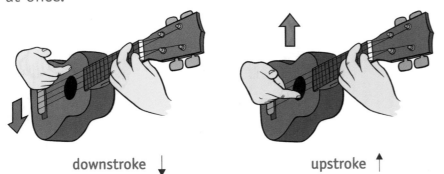

downstroke ↓   upstroke ↑

For each song you played a particular *strumming pattern*, like the one below:

Practise this pattern several times to remind yourself, using just an F chord.

Before you begin to sing and play each song, try saying the words out loud and in rhythm. Clap a steady beat as you do this, and then practise the strumming pattern slowly at first, until you are confident.

You've also learnt how to play different chords by changing where you place your left-hand fingers. The chords to play for each song are shown by chord symbols above the music. The chord shapes below are ones you have already learnt. Play through them to remind yourself of how they are played.

Now you are ready to play the next three songs.

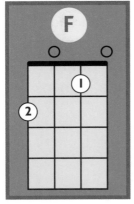

F major (F)

C seven (C7)

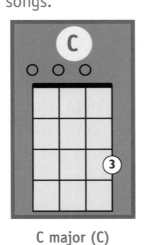

C major (C)

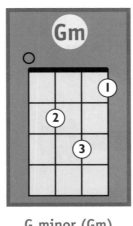

G minor (Gm)

4

La Cucaracha (The Cockroach)

Strumming pattern:

Play this stumming pattern throughout the whole song, changing chords where shown.

Can you remember learning about *repeat signs*. They tell you to play the music between them twice. The first time through you play the *1st-time bar* (the bar with the number 1 above it) and the second time through you jump to the *2nd-time bar*.

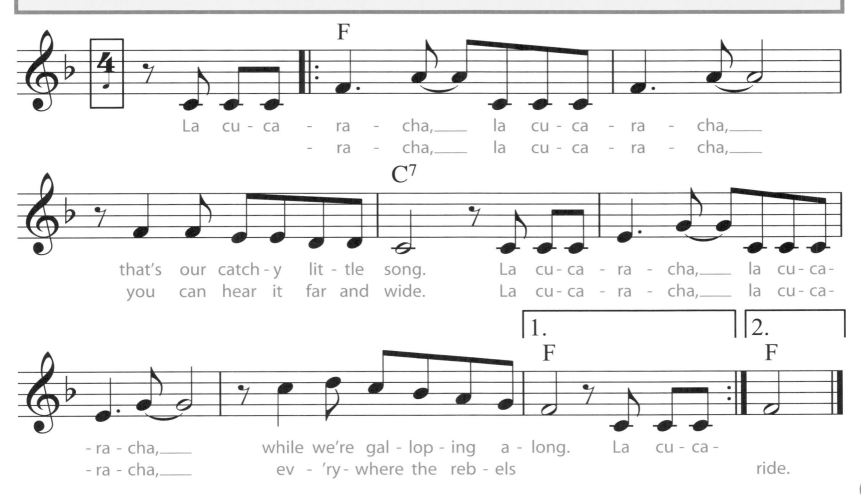

La cu - ca - ra - cha,___ la cu - ca - ra - cha,___
- ra - cha,___ la cu - ca - ra - cha,___

that's our catch-y lit-tle song. La cu-ca - ra - cha,___ la cu-ca-
you can hear it far and wide. La cu-ca - ra - cha,___ la cu-ca-

- ra - cha,___ while we're gal-lop-ing a - long. La cu-ca-
- ra - cha,___ ev - 'ry-where the reb-els ride.

Chiapanecas

Strumming pattern:

This pattern uses two upstrokes in a row, so practise it slowly to begin with, until you are confident.

Be prepared for the fast chord changes in the last two bars of this song!

Idea:
Try tapping your ukulele body (softly) in the crotchet rests of the chorus.

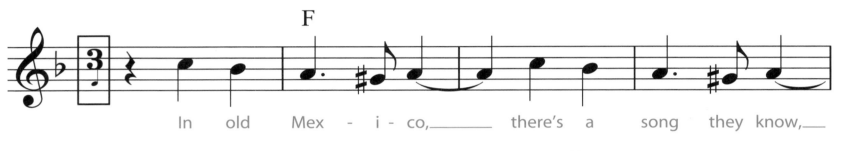

In old Mex - i - co,_____ there's a song they know,_____

____ ev - 'ry - where you hear_____ 'Chia - pan - e - cas!'_____ It's an

ea - sy thing,_____ when you get the swing,_____ clap your

Skip To My Lou

Strumming pattern:  *or:*

Say the words to this song out loud and in rhythm.
Clap a steady beat as you do this. Strum a downstroke on these beats (every minim). Now, try the alternative strumming pattern, filling in the offbeats.

Idea:
Half of your class could strum and the other half sing whilst clapping a steady minim beat.

Some familiar chords

Here are two more chord shapes that you already know from *Book 1* — D minor and G7.
Make sure you are confident with them before playing the next four songs.

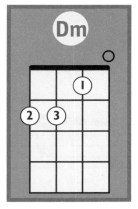

D minor (Dm)

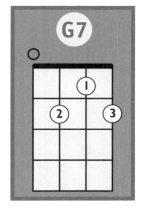

G seven (G7)

You will soon be using more and more chords, and you might find that you occasionally need to remind yourself how to play them.

A quick reference point is the 'Guide to Chord Shapes' at the back of this book, which lists all the chord shapes you need for *Books 1* and *2*.

Clementine

Strumming pattern:

This tune uses the dotted rhythm 𝅘𝅥𝅭 𝅘𝅥𝅮 —a dotted quaver (¾ beat) followed by a semiquaver (¼ beat). Do you remember this from *Book 1*? It should sound like a skip.

Idea: Ask a friend to tap a tambourine on the 2nd and 3rd beat of every bar.

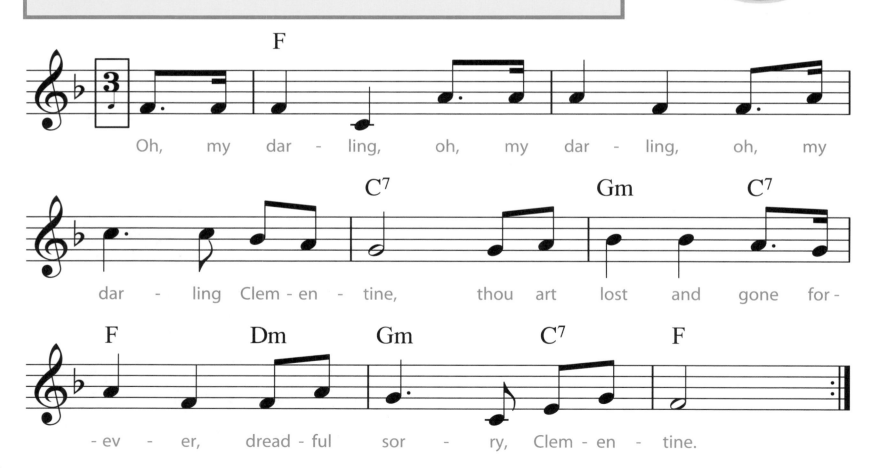

Oh, my dar - ling, oh, my dar - ling, oh, my dar - ling Clem - en - tine, thou art lost and gone for - ev - er, dread - ful sor - ry, Clem - en - tine.

I Saw Three Ships

Strumming pattern:

Notice how the six quavers in each bar are grouped as two sets of three. This is called *compound time* — listen to how it sounds.

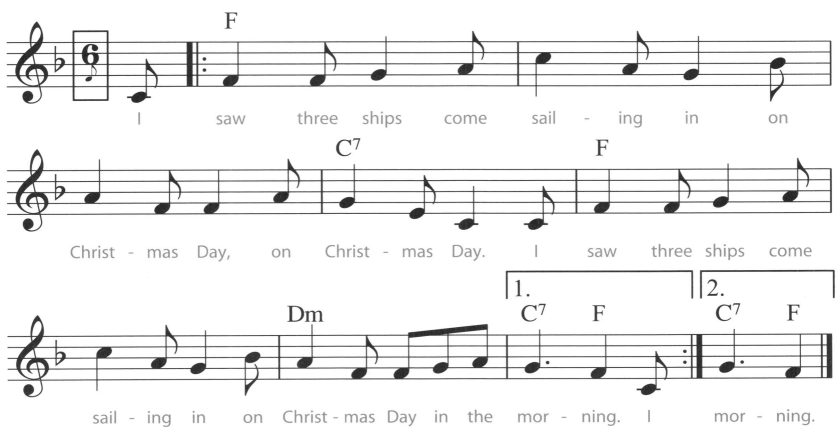

The Big Rock Candy Mountain

Strumming pattern:

Practise this strumming pattern slowly to begin with, being careful not to strum on the 2nd beat of each bar!

In the Big Rock Can - dy Moun - tains, there's a

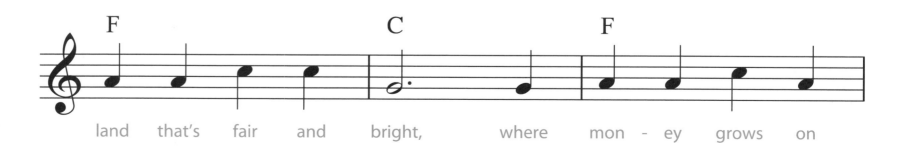

land that's fair and bright, where mon - ey grows on

Linstead Market

Strumming pattern:

This strumming pattern is *syncopated*, meaning that one or more of the weaker beats of the bar are given an accent (or stress) that they wouldn't usually be given. In this case, there is a strong downstroke on the '&' after beat 2.

Practise the pattern slowly at first.

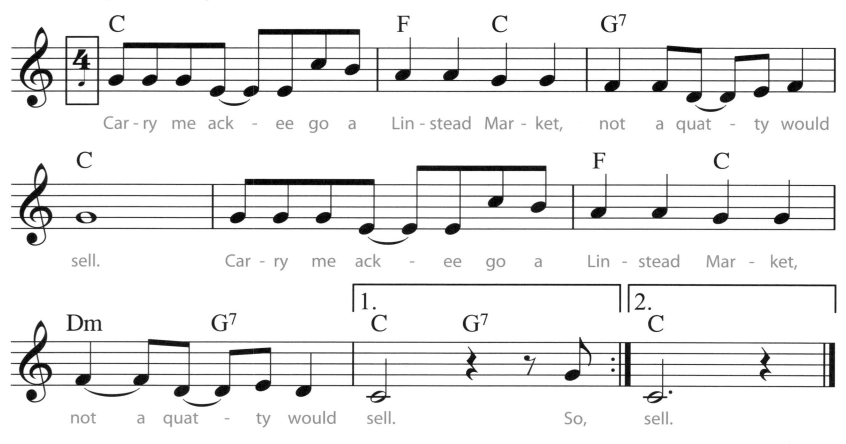

Some new chords

Here are four brand new chords for you to learn — a new seventh chord (A7) and three new major chords.

For each new chord, carefully position your fingers as shown in the chord boxes below. Press down firmly and then practise strumming the chord, using a strumming pattern of your choice.

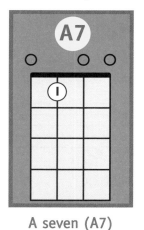

A seven (A7)

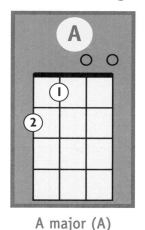

A major (A)

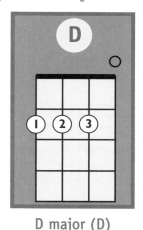

D major (D)

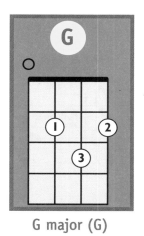

G major (G)

Here is a reminder of three more chords you learnt in *Book 1*.

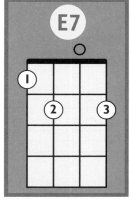

E seven (E7)

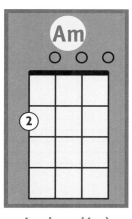

A minor (Am)

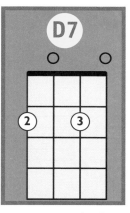

D seven (D7)

Practise moving between the following chord shapes. You'll be using these progressions in the next few songs.

C → A7 → Dm

A → E7 → A → D

A → A7 → D

F → G → C

Once you have practised these changes, play four downstrokes on each chord and try to keep a steady tempo.

15

Buffalo Gals

Strumming pattern:

Notice that this uses the same strumming pattern that you mastered for *The Big Rock Candy Mountain*.

Idea:
Now try using one of the the strumming patterns from *Skip To My Lou*.

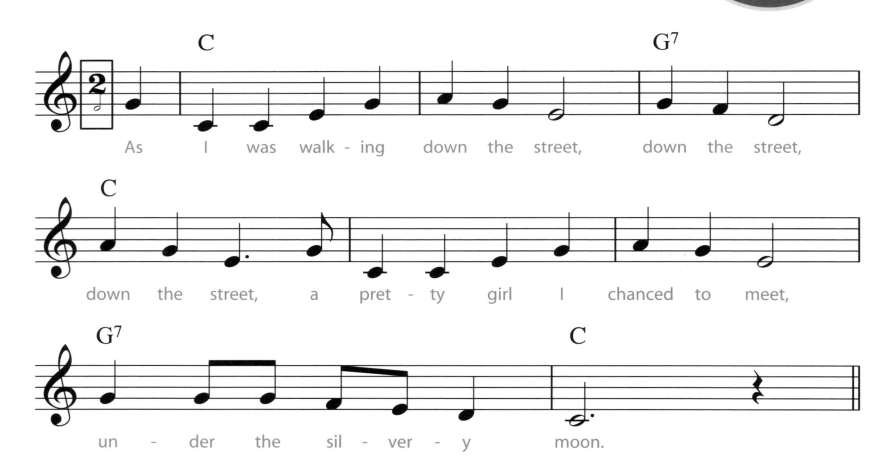

As I was walk - ing down the street, down the street,

down the street, a pret - ty girl I chanced to meet,

un - der the sil - ver - y moon.

The Grand Old Duke Of York

Strumming pattern:

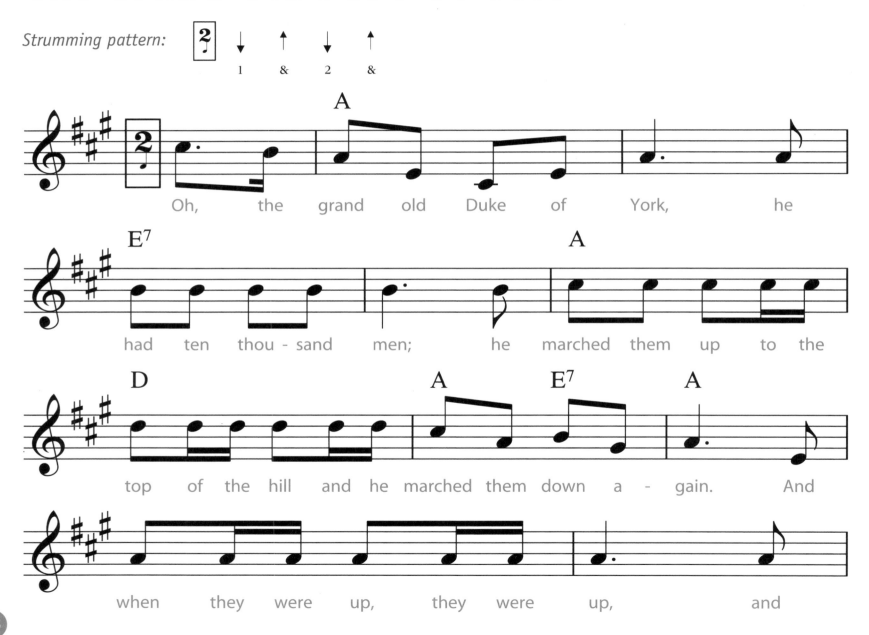

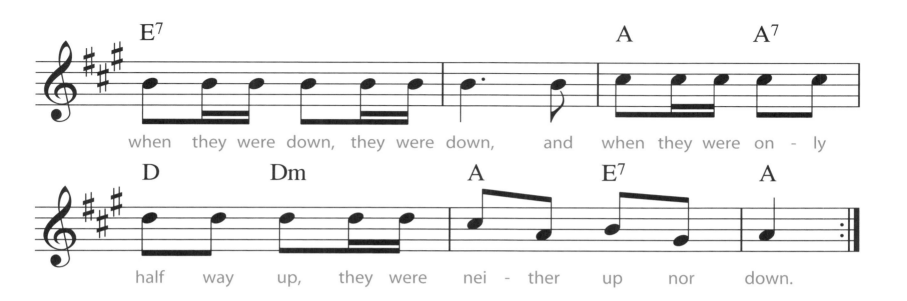

when they were down, they were down, and when they were on - ly

half way up, they were nei - ther up nor down.

Little Brown Jug

Strumming pattern:

Watch out for the *repeat signs* and *1st-* and *2nd-time bars* in this song.
Make sure you know what they tell you to do before you start to play.

My wife and I live all a - lone in a lit - tle log hut we
She loves rain and I love sun, I'll tell you what, we've

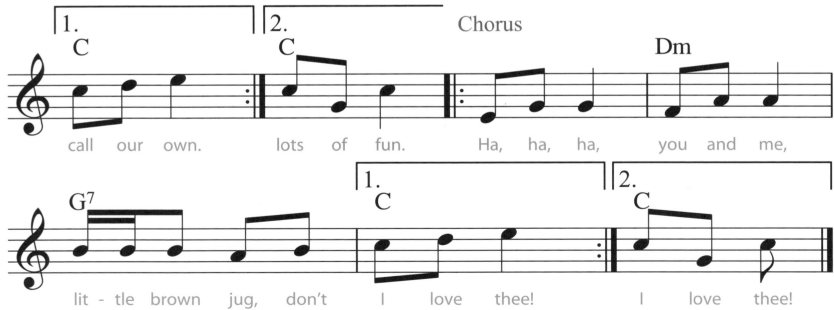

call our own. lots of fun. Ha, ha, ha, you and me,

lit - tle brown jug, don't I love thee! I love thee!

Pop Goes The Weasel

Strumming pattern:

Watch out for the fast strumming on the last three quaver beats of the pattern!

Half a pound of tup-pen-ny rice, half a pound of trea - cle,

that's the way the mon - ey goes: pop, goes the wea - sel!

We Shall Overcome

Fingerpicking

Now you are going to learn a new and exciting type of ukulele playing. *Fingerpicking* involves plucking the strings individually to create a repetitive broken chord pattern.

Let's begin by using your thumb *(T)* and first finger *(f1)*. The diagram below shows you which strings to play and whether to use your thumb or first finger. The counts for one bar are written out underneath to show you when the strings should be played. Practise this pattern slowly at first, using an F major chord and keeping a very steady rhythm. Gradually speed up as you become more confident.

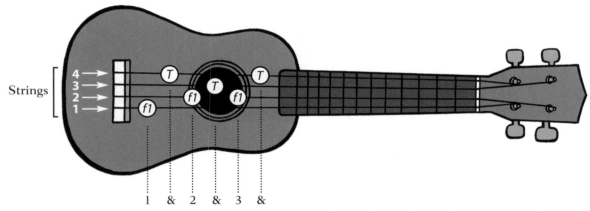

The pattern can also be written like this:

For each count there is a string number (for example, **1**) followed by a finger number (for example, *f1*), showing you which string to play and which finger to play it with.

Once you have mastered the pattern, you should repeat it throughout the whole song, changing chords as usual where shown.

Lavender's Blue

Use the fingerpicking pattern you have just learnt to accompany this song. Repeat the pattern in every bar — the strings you play on each quaver beat are shown above the music to remind you.

A new fingerpicking pattern

Now try learning this fingerpicking pattern. Like the previous pattern, this uses just your thumb *(T)* and first finger *(f1)*, although this time you begin the pattern with your thumb.

Practise the new pattern slowly at first, using a G major chord and keeping a very steady rhythm. Gradually speed up as you become more confident.

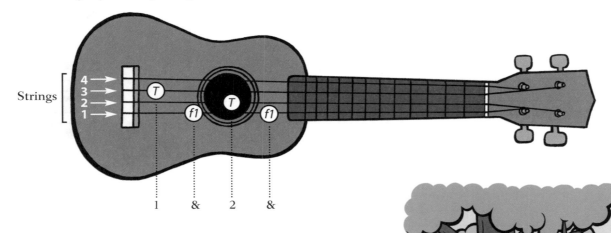

It can also be written like this:

(**3**T) (**1**f1) (**2**T) (**1**f1)

1   &   2   &

Use this fingerpicking pattern to accompany the next song.

Down By The Riverside

Finnegan's Wake

Use the same fingerpicking pattern as *Down By The Riverside* to accompany this song:

Or, you could try this *stumming pattern*:

Two more new chords

Here are two more new chords for you to learn — a *diminished seventh* chord and a new major chord. Diminshed seventh chords are used to create musical tension and lead to the next chord. It sounds hard, but is actually very easy to play!

Carefully position your fingers as shown in the chord boxes below and, pressing down firmly, try strumming each chord using a strumming pattern of your choice. Notice that for the B♭ major chord, your first finger has to hold down two strings at the same time.

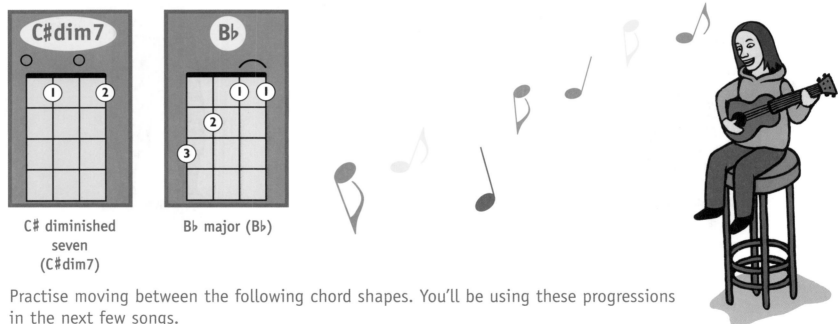

C# diminished
seven
(C#dim7)

B♭ major (B♭)

Practise moving between the following chord shapes. You'll be using these progressions in the next few songs.

C ⟶ C#dim7 ⟶ Dm

Gm ⟶ B♭

C ⟶ B♭ ⟶ Am ⟶ Dm

F ⟶ B♭ ⟶ G7

Once you have practised these changes, play four downstrokes on each chord and try to keep a steady tempo.

You'll be strumming again for the next two songs, while you get used to playing the new chords.

The Mocking Bird (Choucoune)

Strumming pattern:

If you find this strumming pattern tricky, just strum downwards on each beat of the bar.

Play this whole song twice through (repeating both times).

The Animals Went In Two By Two

Strumming pattern: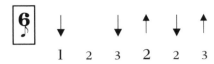

Practise this strumming pattern slowly to being with.

Idea:
Can you find another strumming pattern in this book to use here?

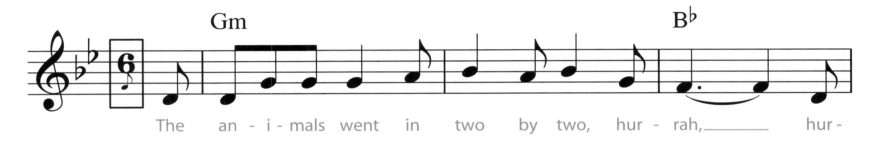

The an - i - mals went in two by two, hur - rah,_____ hur -

- rah!_____ The an - i - mals went in two by two, hur -

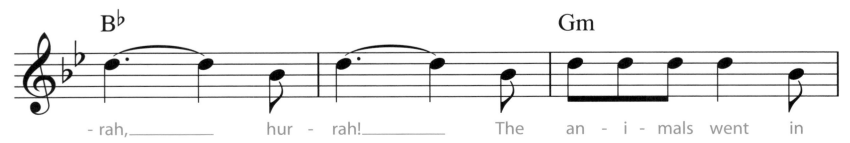

- rah,_____ hur - rah!_____ The an - i - mals went in

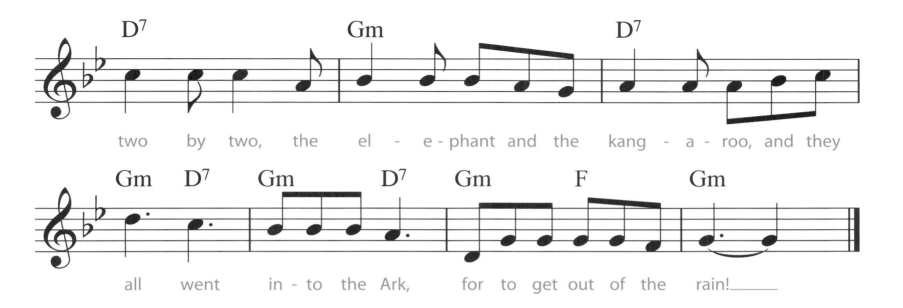

two   by   two,   the   el - e -phant and the   kang - a - roo, and they

all   went   in - to   the Ark,   for   to   get out   of   the   rain!____

A new fingerpicking pattern

The fingerpicking pattern opposite uses your 2nd finger *(f2)* as well as your thumb *(T)* and first finger *(f1)*.

Try practising it slowly to begin with.

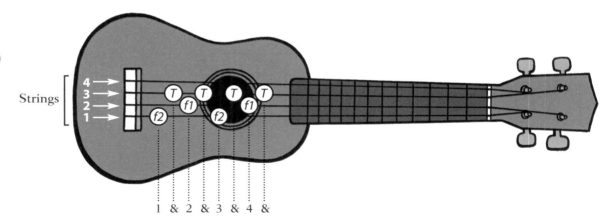

It can also be written like this: (**1***f2*) (**3***T*) (**2***f1*) (**3***T*) (**1***f2*) (**3***T*) (**2***f1*) (**3***T*)

                                                1   &   2   &   3   &   4   &

The Wraggle-Taggle Gypsies

Use the fingerpicking pattern you have just learnt (on page 33) to accompany this song.

Fingerpicking pattern: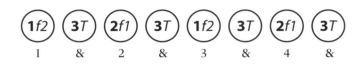

There were three gyp - sies come to my door, and down - stairs ran this lady, oh! One sang high and a- noth-er sang low, and the oth-er sang bon - ny, bon - ny Bis - cay, oh!

He's Got The Whole World In His Hands

Strumming pattern:

Once you are confident playing this song, try the fingerpicking pattern that you learnt for *The Wraggle-Taggle Gypsies*, but remember to swing the quavers this time!

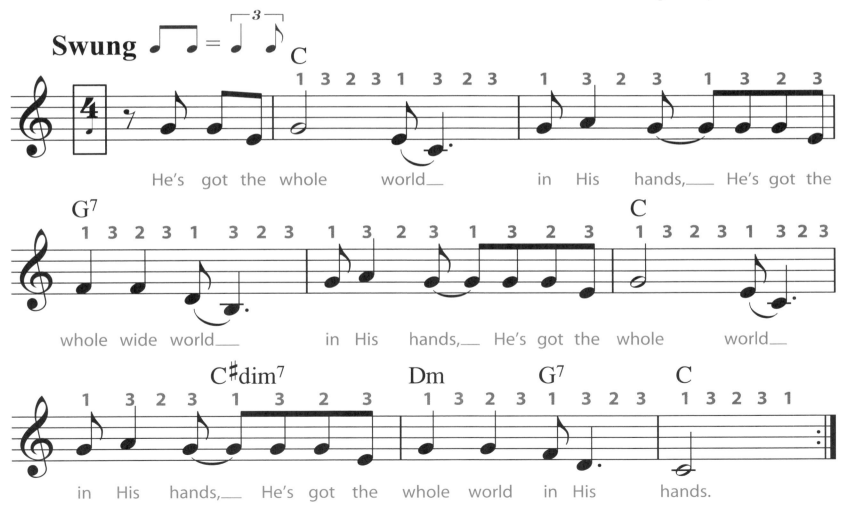

He's got the whole world___ in His hands,___ He's got the whole wide world___ in His hands,___ He's got the whole world___ in His hands,___ He's got the whole world in His hands.

This Train Is Bound For Glory

It's up to you whether you accompany a song with fingerpicking or strumming. This song works well with strumming.

If you've forgotten any of the chords, don't forget the a handy guide on page 40.

We Wish You A Merry Christmas

Fingerpicking pattern: (**1f2**) (**3T**) (**2f1**) (**4T**) (**2f1**) (**3T**) Practise this pattern very slowly to begin with.

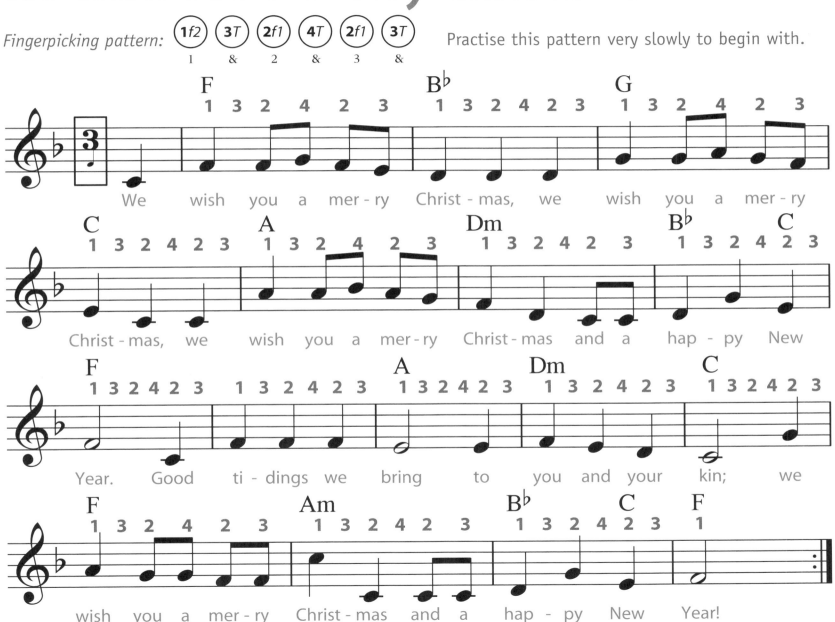

Simple Gifts

Fingerpicking pattern: (**3**T) (**1**f1) (**2**T) (**1**f1) (**3**T) (**1**f1) (**2**T) (**1**f1)
　　　　　　　　　1　　&　　2　　&　　3　　&　　4　　&

This uses the same sequence used in the fingerpicking pattern for *Down By The Riverside*.

If you wanted to, you could always strum to accompany this song.

'Tis the gift to be sim-ple, 'tis the gift to be free, 'tis the

gift to come down where we ought to be. And

when we find our-selves in the place just right, 'twill be in the val - ley of

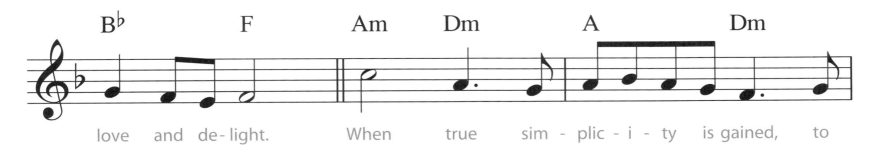

love and de-light. When true sim - plic - i - ty is gained, to

bow and to bend, we shan't be a - shamed; to turn, turn will

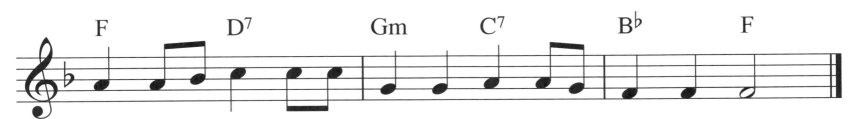

be our de-light, 'til by turn - ing, turn - ing we come round right.

Guide to chord shapes

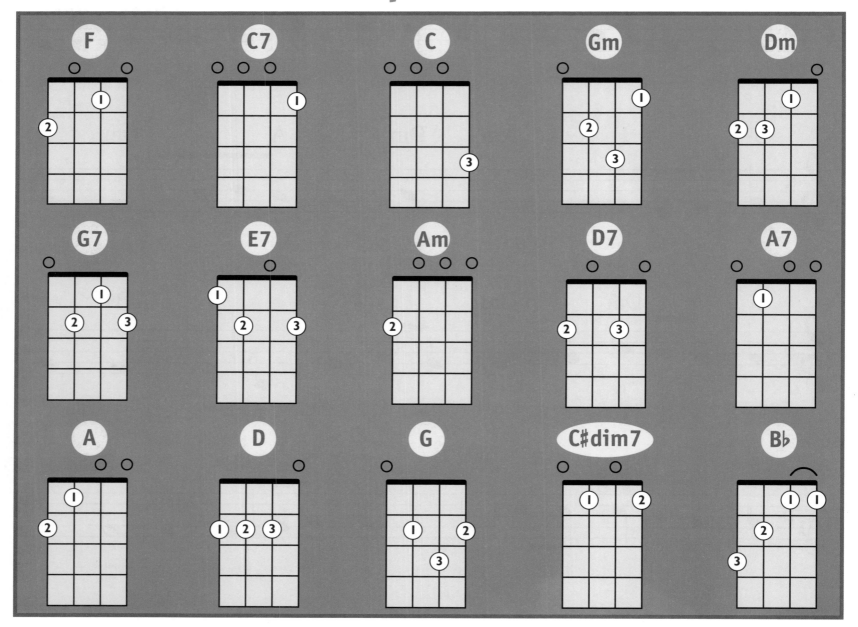